U0266019

晚霞项链

【美】苏·凯斯尔◎著
【美】佩奇·伊斯特伯恩·欧鲁克◎绘
范晓星◎译

天津出版传媒集团
新蕾出版社

图书在版编目（CIP）数据

晚霞项链/(美)凯斯尔(Kassirer,S.)著;(美)欧鲁克(O'Rourke,P.E.)绘;范晓星译.
—天津:新蕾出版社,2014.1(2024.12重印)
(数学帮帮忙·互动版)
书名原文:What's Next，Nina?
ISBN 978-7-5307-5902-8

Ⅰ.①晚…

Ⅱ.①凯…②欧…③范…

Ⅲ.①数学–儿童读物

Ⅳ.①O1–49

中国版本图书馆CIP数据核字(2013)第270439号

What's Next, Nina?　by Sue Kassirer;
Illustrated by Page Eastburn O'Rourke.
Copyright © 2001 by Kane Press, Inc.
All rights reserved, including the right of reproduction in whole or in part in any form. This edition published by arrangement with Kane Press, Inc. New York, NY, represented by Lerner Publishing Group through TheChoiceMaker Korea Co. Agency.
Simplified Chinese translation copyright © 2014 by New Buds Publishing House (Tianjin) Limited Company
ALL RIGHTS RESERVED
本书中文简体版专有出版权经由中华版权代理中心授予新蕾出版社(天津)有限公司。未经许可,不得以任何方式复制或抄袭本书的任何部分。
津图登字:02-2012-236

出版发行:天津出版传媒集团
　　　　　新蕾出版社

http://www.newbuds.com.cn

地　　址:天津市和平区西康路35号(300051)
出 版 人:马玉秀
电　　话:总编办(022)23332422
　　　　　发行部(022)23332679　23332351
传　　真:(022)23332422
经　　销:全国新华书店
印　　刷:天津新华印务有限公司
开　　本:787mm×1092mm　1/16
印　　张:3
版　　次:2014年1月第1版　2024年12月第23次印刷
定　　价:12.00元

著作权所有,请勿擅用本书制作各类出版物,违者必究。
如发现印、装质量问题,影响阅读,请与本社发行部联系调换。
地址:天津市和平区西康路35号
电话:(022)23332351　邮编:300051

无处不在的数学

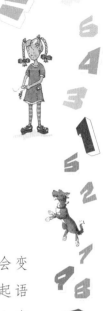

资深编辑　卢　江

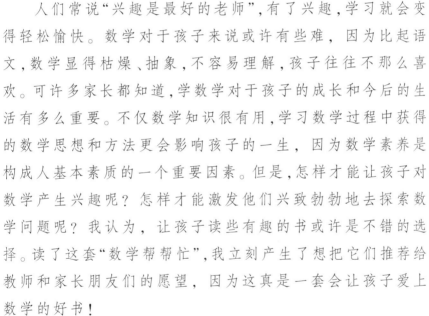

　　人们常说"兴趣是最好的老师"，有了兴趣，学习就会变得轻松愉快。数学对于孩子来说或许有些难，因为比起语文，数学显得枯燥、抽象，不容易理解，孩子往往不那么喜欢。可许多家长都知道，学数学对于孩子的成长和今后的生活有多么重要。不仅数学知识很有用，学习数学过程中获得的数学思想和方法更会影响孩子的一生，因为数学素养是构成人基本素质的一个重要因素。但是，怎样才能让孩子对数学产生兴趣呢？怎样才能激发他们兴致勃勃地去探索数学问题呢？我认为，让孩子读些有趣的书或许是不错的选择。读了这套"数学帮帮忙"，我立刻产生了想把它们推荐给教师和家长朋友们的愿望，因为这真是一套会让孩子爱上数学的好书！

　　这套有趣的图书从美国引进，原出版者是美国资深教育专家。每本书讲述一个孩子们生活中的故事，由故事中出现的问题自然地引入一个数学知识，然后通过运用数学知识解决问题。比如，从帮助外婆整理散落的纽扣引出分类，从为小狗记录藏骨头的地点引出空间方位等等。故事素材全部来源于孩子们的真实生活，不是童话，不是幻想，而是鲜活的生活实例。正是这些发生在孩子身边的故事，让孩子们懂得，数学无处不在并且非常有用；这些鲜活的实例也使得抽象的概念更易于理解，更容易激发孩子学习数学的兴趣，让他们逐渐爱上数学。这样的教育思想和方法与我国近年来提倡的数学教育理念是十分吻合的！

这是一套适合5~8岁孩子阅读的书，书中的有趣情节和生动的插画可以将抽象的数学问题直观化、形象化，为孩子的思维活动提供具体形象的支持。如果亲子共读的话，家长可以带领孩子推测情节的发展，探讨解决难题的办法，让孩子在愉悦的氛围中学到知识和方法。

值得教师和家长朋友们注意的是，在每本书的后面，出版者还加入了"互动课堂"及"互动练习"，一方面通过一些精心设计的活动让孩子巩固新学到的数学知识，进一步体会知识的含义和实际应用；另一方面帮助家长指导孩子阅读，体会故事中数学之外的道理，逐步提升孩子的阅读理解能力。

我相信孩子读过这套书后一定会明白，原来，数学不是烦恼，不是包袱，数学真能帮大忙！

今天,有一场盛大的派对,可我能穿的只有这条又旧又丑的裙子。我该怎么办呢?

请您光临
在萨沃伊酒店举办的
蒂芬妮小姐的生日派对
期待您的回复!
请致电555-1111

　　我觉得这全是我自己的错。我本来去商场是想买条新裙子,却看到了一个特别炫的滑板,我好想要啊。

　　"不行,妮娜。"妈妈说,"你或者要滑板,或者要新裙子,但不能两样都买。"

所以我就说:"好吧,我就穿旧裙子去参加派对吧。"我当时以为旧裙子不会那么糟糕,直到今天……

　　试来试去,只有这条丑巴巴的裙子还合身。可我怎么能穿这么平常的衣服去参加那么隆重的派对呢?别人都会穿自己最漂亮的衣服去的!

这时，我看见姐姐茉莉亚的梳妆台上有一条很漂亮的项链。天蓝色、淡紫色、粉红色和橘黄色的珠子穿在一起，就像晚霞的颜色。

我马上戴上项链试试效果，镜子里的我立刻变得神采奕奕。我一定要戴这条项链去。

　　我应该先问问茉莉亚可不可以把项链借给我，可她很可能会拒绝我。不管怎么说，我现在不能打扰她，她正忙着跟朋友听唱片呢。对！我觉得我可以借她的项链戴戴，然后在她还没想起来之前再放回去！

我踮着脚尖走到走廊。好！没被发现！于是我猛冲下楼。

我披上大衣，戴上围巾。"准备好啦，妈妈！"我大喊。

9

果然，来参加派对的女孩们个个光彩照人。没有人留意我穿了一件那么普通的裙子。他们光顾着欣赏我的项链了，每个人都美慕极了。

只有艾丽丝一个人知道那条项链是我姐姐的。艾丽丝是我最好的朋友，我俩无话不说。

我们在派对上玩得很开心：有魔术师从帽子里变出一只又一只小白兔，有味道特别的奶昔，还有像城堡一样大的蛋糕！

我和艾丽丝正要回家,突然觉得脖子上痒痒的,用手一挠,不!不可能!项链断了!珠子飞得到处都是。

　　大家都追着去捡珠子。我一个人呆呆地站着，手里
抓着项链上仅剩的四颗小珠子。我满脑子想的全是：我
该怎么跟姐姐说？我为什么要偷偷拿她的项链呢？

"我觉得我们已经都捡齐啦！"艾丽丝说，"都捡好了！让我妈妈带咱们去那家新开的串珠店吧。那儿也许有人会帮我们把项链复原的。"

"你觉得能复原吗？"我问道。

"当然啦！"艾丽丝说，"串珠店专门就是做这个的嘛！"

那么说，还有希望！我谢过大家帮我捡珠子，然后和艾丽丝一起向串珠店出发了。

这家商店真的不一般！墙上挂满了各式各样的漂亮项链、耳环和手链。店里还有许许多多的小橱格，里面放着各式各样的珠子：有大有小、色彩斑斓，形状也是五花八门！

可现在，要是我还能记起姐姐的项链是什么样的……

17

"孩子们，你们想买什么？"店主贝西阿姨问。

我把事情一股脑儿地跟她说了一遍。"这些珠子全都乱套了。"我说，"只剩下这四颗没有掉下来。"

"这四颗珠子可以给我们一些提示。"贝西阿姨说。"看这个，"她取出一条手链，"蓝色，蓝色，红色，金色；蓝色，蓝色，红色，金色……"

"这是按规律穿成的呀！"我说，"我觉得我的项链也是按某种规律穿起来的，对吗？"

"没错！"贝西阿姨说。

　　贝西阿姨把我的珠子放进一个小篮子，然后递给我一个看上去很好玩的托盘。她说："你可以用这个，先找到珠子的排列规律。"

　　我深深地吸了一口气。"规律，规律……"我说道，"规律会是什么呢？"

　　"再来一颗紫色的？"艾丽丝问。

　　"不对，蓝色的珠子还有那么多呢。"

"是有好多蓝色的！"艾丽丝说。

我试着摆上一颗蓝色的。

我又一颗接一颗地摆上去。

"有门儿！"艾丽丝也说。

哎哟！那颗紫色的珠子跑哪儿去了？

艾丽丝和我试了一遍又一遍：紫色，紫色，蓝色，蓝色，蓝色，蓝色，哎呀！"我现在就知道晚上我会做什么梦了！"我说。

"我也是！"艾丽丝说。

终于，所有蓝色和紫色的珠子都用光了。"然后呢？"艾丽丝问。

　　"粉色和橘色的珠子。"我说，"可是我记不得它们是怎么排的了。"

　　"我也记不清了。"艾丽丝说，"我妈妈一会儿就要来接我了，不早了。"

　　我往窗外一看，果然，太阳都下山了。

　　"我想起来了！"我喊道，"这条项链曾让我联想到晚霞！"

"是呀！"艾丽丝说，"还有一颗金色的珠子，就像是太阳！"

　　"可金色的珠子不在这儿。"我嘟哝道，"一定是丢了。"我一屁股坐进椅子里。

　　"没关系！"艾丽丝说，"你忘了？我们现在是在串珠店里呀！"

23

　　艾丽丝给我找来很多金色的珠子。有一颗跟原先的一模一样！我把这颗珠子放在托盘上。"现在呢……"我说。

　　"粉色和橘色。"艾丽丝说，"就像晚霞的颜色。"

　　我把所有粉色和橘色的珠子都摆好。

　　万岁！我们成功了！

艾丽丝帮我用丝线把珠子穿起来，又帮我把项链系好。

"和新的一样！"我说。

回到家，我蹑手蹑脚地走上楼，把项链放回姐姐茉莉亚的梳妆台上。你们会以为我现在总算松了一口气，对吧？并不是。我根本就不应该偷偷拿走姐姐的项链，连问都没问一声。

"派对怎么样？"茉莉亚问我。

　　"哦，姐姐，"我深深地吸了一口气，开口道，"对不起，我拿了你的项链戴去参加蒂芬妮的派对，而且我没有问过你。你的项链太好看了，我的裙子太丑了……"

"当然好看啦！"茱莉亚说，"所以我才要给你这条项链呀。可是你跑得太快了，我都没来得及告诉你！"

　　"什么？"我说，"项链是给我的？"我高兴得都不会说话了。

　　"我也给自己买了一条。"茱莉亚说，"一模一样，看到了吧。"

我目不转睛地盯着姐姐的项链。"嗯,几乎一模一样……"我说,"只不过,你的这条是 5 个蓝珠,1 个紫珠,中间的一颗是……"

　　"哈哈！你真是个找规律的高手！"茉莉
亚说，"你可以自己做首饰了。你知道咱们
镇上新开了一家串珠店吗？"

我大笑起来。然后，我告诉茉莉亚我是
怎么变得擅长找规律的。

规 律

我会自己画一些有规律的图形,你也来试试! 很好玩哟!

颜色规律

规律:绿,绿,绿,黄,黄,红

大小规律

规律:小,大,小,小,大,大

颜色和大小规律

规律:小黄,小黄,大黄,小紫,小紫,大紫

颜色和形状规律

规律:红圆,黄方,蓝圆,绿方

亲爱的家长朋友，请您和孩子一起完成下面这些内容，会有更大的收获哟！

提高阅读能力

- 阅读封面，包括书名等内容。和孩子聊聊，封面画了什么？请孩子说说妮娜的袜子是什么图案，并预测一下故事的内容，是否和规律有关。

- 读过故事之后，请孩子看第 18 页。贝西阿姨是如何形容项链串珠的规律？鼓励孩子描述第 16~17 页上画的各种项链的排列规律。

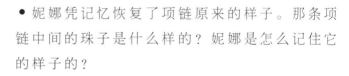

- 妮娜凭记忆恢复了项链原来的样子。那条项链中间的珠子是什么样的？妮娜是怎么记住它的样子的？

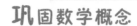

巩固数学概念

- 请找出第 32 页练习中图案的规律，先找第一、三、四行"颜色"的规律。再找二、三行"大小"的规律。最后，找出最后一行"形状"的规律。请孩子说出每行后面应该接着什么颜色、大小和形状。

- 在第 29 页上有两条项链，它们一样吗？有哪里不一样？你觉得妮娜的姐姐发现这两条项链的不同了吗？

生活中的数学

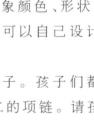

- 在你的家里，找找什么地方有重复规律的图案，比如一些日常用品。家长可以给孩子一些线索，比如："我在盘子上找到了一组有规律的图案"，或者"我看到了红、绿、红、绿的图案"，就连图画书上也能找到很多有规律的图案。

- 找一张大纸，用带图案的模板，想象颜色、形状，然后按规律在纸上重复图形，这样就可以自己设计好看的包装纸了。

- 为孩子准备一些塑料或者木质珠子。孩子们都喜欢自己把珠子穿起来，设计独一无二的项链。请孩子描述自己的项链规律是什么？

我和妮娜又做了一条漂亮的项链，你能说出它的排列规律吗？

再次光临贝西阿姨的串珠店，真高兴呀！

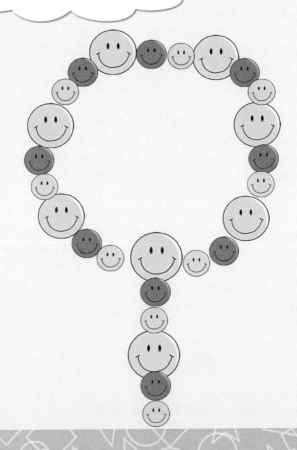

你从颜色、大小、数量、形状等方面去观察，可以发现一些规律。试着找到并说出下面两条项链的规律。

观察下面的排列有什么规律，请你说出它的规律并按规律把正确的图形填到空白框里。

拿起你的彩笔，自己设计一条有规律的项链吧！

找一找　说一说

仔细观察麦琪送给妮娜的糖果屋,你能找出其中的规律吗?

魔术师变出了很多有规律的东西，横线上应该是什么图案呢？在正确的图案上打上"√"。

妮娜和茱莉亚用纽扣宝盒里的宝贝纽扣摆出了很多有规律的图案，请圈出每行中有规律的一组。

你能把下面的宝贝纽扣有规律地涂上颜色吗？

我发现马路上信号灯的变换是有规律的。

我发现每个星期都在重复着从星期一到星期天这个规律。

星期一	星期二	星期三	星期四	星期五	星期六	星期天
四月7	8	9	10	11	12	13

星期一	星期二	星期三	星期四	星期五	星期六	星期天
14	15	16	17	18	19	20

星期一	星期二	星期三	星期四	星期五	星期六	星期天
21	22	23	24	25	26	27

星期一	星期二	星期三	星期四	星期五	星期六	星期天
28	29	30	五月1	2	3	4

小朋友，你还发现了生活中的哪些规律,快来说一说吧!

互动练习1：

这条项链是以"1个大笑脸、2个小笑脸"为一组不断重复出现的。

项坠是以"1个黄色大笑脸、1个红色中笑脸和1个绿色小笑脸"为一组不断重复出现的。

互动练习2：

以1个红圆形、1个黄心形、1个蓝五角星为一组不断重复出现。

以1朵红花、1朵黄花为一组不断重复出现。

以1个三角形、2个圆形、3个正方形为一组不断重复出现。

苹果的数量不变，梨的数量逐次加1个。

互动练习3~4：略

互动练习5：

互动练习6：

互动练习7：略

（习题设计：鹿　美）

What's Next, Nina?

It's today—the big fancy party. And all I've got to wear is a plain old dress.

What am I going to do?

I guess it's my own fault. I went shopping or a new dress, but then I saw a cool skateboard. And I really wanted it.

"Sorry, Nina," Mom said, "you can get a skateboard or a new dress—not both."

So I said, "Okay, I'll just wear one of my old dresses to the party." That didn't seem so bad. Until today.

It turns out the only dress that still fits is this icky plain one. How can I go like this? Everybody else will be wearing their fanciest party clothes!

Then I see a necklace on my sister Julia's dresser. It's beautiful. There are sky blue and misty purple beads, and pearly pink and orange ones. Sunset colors.

Quickly, I try the necklace on—and right away, I look fancy. I've just got to wear it.

I should ask Julia if I can borrow it—but she'll probably say no. Anyway, I shouldn't bother her right now. She's busy playing CDs with her friends. Hey! I'll bet I can borrow the necklace and put it back before she even misses it!

I tiptoe into the hall. Good! The coast is clear! I make a mad dash down the stairs.

I throw on my coat and scarf. "Ready, Mom!" I call out.

Sure enough, all the girls at the party look fancy. But no one notices that my dress is plain. They're all too busy admiring my necklace. Everyone is crazy about it.

Only Alice knows that it's my sister's. Alice is my best friend. We tell each other everything.

We have a great time at the party. There's a magician who pulls rabbits out of a hat, a special ice-cream punch, and a cake that looks like a castle!

Alice and I are ready to leave when I feel a tickle on my neck. I reach up. No! It can't be! The necklace is breaking! Beads are flying all over the place.

Everyone runs after them. I just stand there holding onto what's left of the necklace—four little beads. All I can think is, "What will I tell Julia? Why did I ever take it?"

"I think we've got them all!"says Alice. "Let's ask my mom to drop us at that new bead store. Maybe someone there can help you put it back together."

"Do you think they could?"I ask.

"Sure!"says Alice."Beads are their business!"

Then there's hope! I thank everyone for helping, and off we go.

What a store! The walls are covered with beautiful necklaces, earrings, and bracelets.There are lots of cubbies filled with beads. And the beads are every size, color, and shape in the universe!

Now, if I can just remember how the necklace looked...

"Can I help you girls?"asks Betsy, the owner.

I spill out my story—and my beads. "They're all mixed up,"I tell her, "except for these four."

"Those four beads are a clue,"Betsy says.

"Look at this."She holds out a bracelet. "Blue, blue, red, gold. Blue, blue, red, gold..."

"It's a pattern!"I say. "I guess my necklace had one too, right?"

"Exactly!"says Betsy.

Betsy sweeps my beads into a basket and hands me a funny-looking tray."You can use this to work out your pattern,"she says.

I take a deep breath."Pattern...pattern..."I say."How did it go?"

"Another purple?"asks Alice.

"No..., there was more blue,"I say.

"Lots more!"says Alice.

I try a blue bead.

I put down another and another.

"Looking good!"Alice says.

Whoops! Where did that purple bead go?

Alice and I do purple, purple, blue, blue, blue, blue again and again. Whew! "I know what I'll dream about tonight,"I say.

"Me, too!"says Alice.

At last all the blue and purple beads are used up."What's next?"Alice asks.

"The pink and orange beads,"I say."But I don't remember the pattern."

"I don't either,"says Alice."And my mom will be here soon. It's getting late."

I look out the window. Sure enough, the sun is going down.

"That's it!"I shout."The necklace made me think of a sunset!"

"Yes!"says Alice."There was even a gold bead—like the sun."

"But it's not here,"I moan."It must be lost."I slump in my chair.

"No problem,"Alice says."We're in a bead store, remember?"

Alice brings me a whole bunch of gold beads. One is just perfect! I put it in the tray."And now..."I say.

"Pink and then orange,"Alice says,"like in the sunset."

I put down all the pink beads and all the orange beads.

Yay! We did it!

Alice helps me string the beads. Then she fastens the necklace.

"It's as good as new!" I say.

Back home, I tiptoe upstairs and put the necklace on Julia's dresser. You'd think I'd feel okay now, right? But I don't. I never should have taken it—not without asking.

"How was the party?" asks Julia.

"Oh, Julia,"I say. I take a big breath."I'm so sorry I took your necklace and wore it to Tiffany's party, and I didn't ask you, and it was just so beautiful, and my dress was so plain..."

"It sure was!"says Julia. "That's why I got you the necklace. But you ran out of here so fast, I couldn't tell you."

"What?"I say."It was for me?"I can hardly speak.

"I got one for myself, too,"Julia says."It's just the same, see?"

I stare hard at my sister's necklace."Well, it's almost the same...,"I say. "But yours has five blues and one purple. And on the bottom..."

"Wow, you have an eye for patterns! "says Julia."You could make your own jewelry. Did you know there's a brand new bead shop in town?"

I start to laugh. And then I tell Julia just how I got so good at patterns!